T0112252

JOHN ADAMS
AMERICAN BERSERK
FOR SOLO PIANO

HENDON MUSIC

BOOSEY & HAWKES

DISTRIBUTED BY

HAL • LEONARD®
CORPORATION
7777 W. BLUEMOUND RD. P.O. BOX 13819 MILWAUKEE, WI 53213

www.boosey.com
www.halleonard.com

Commissioned for Garrick Ohlsson
by The Carnegie Hall Corporation

Edited by Nicolas Hodges

First performed on February 25, 2002 by Garrick Ohlsson
at Carnegie Hall, New York City

First recorded by Nicolas Hodges
on Nonesuch 79699-2

Duration: 6 minutes

for Garrick

AMERICAN BERSERK

JOHN ADAMS
(2001)

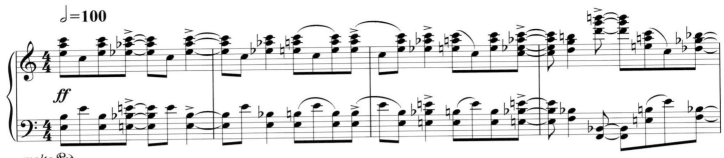

© Copyright 2002, 2007 by Hendon Music, Inc.,
a Boosey & Hawkes company.
Copyright for all countries. All rights reserved.

M-051-24626-7

Printed in U.S.A.

Right hand slightly
softer than than left

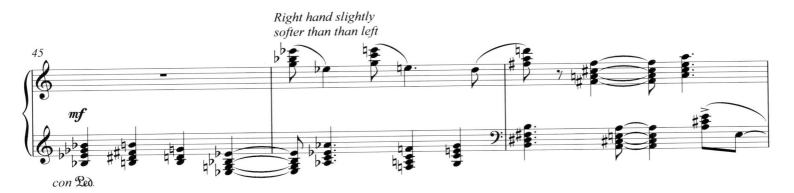

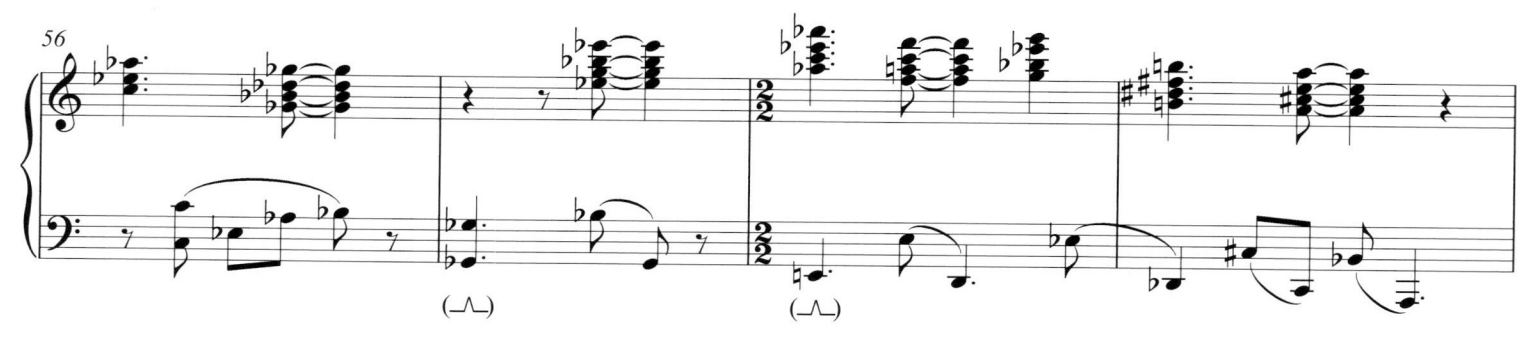

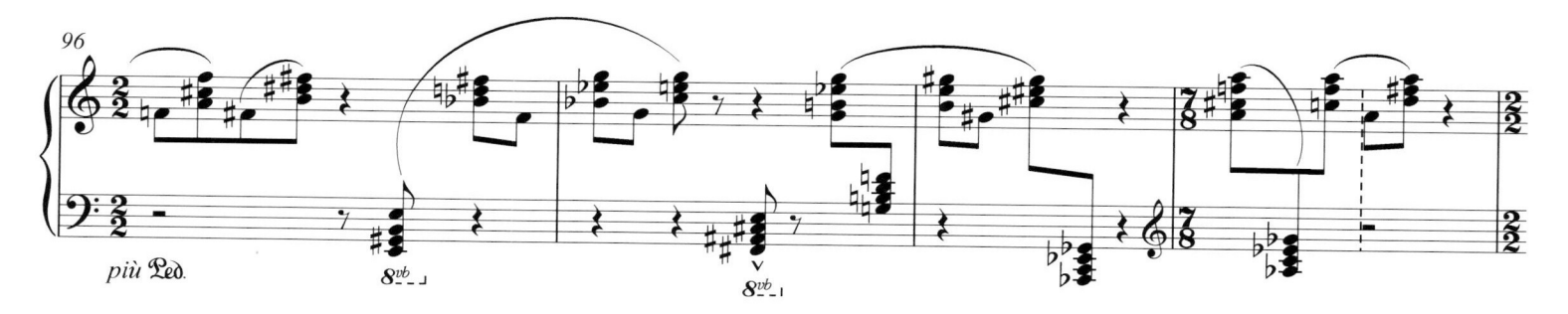

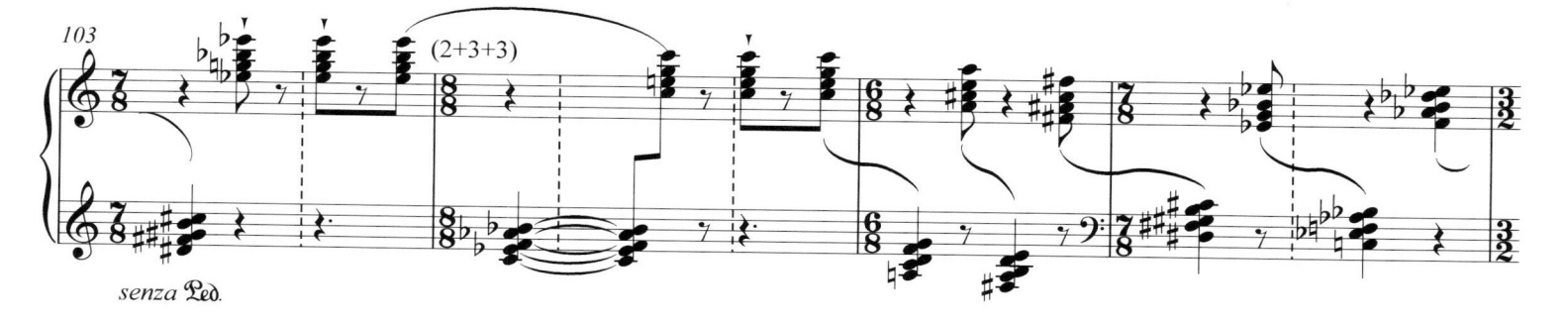

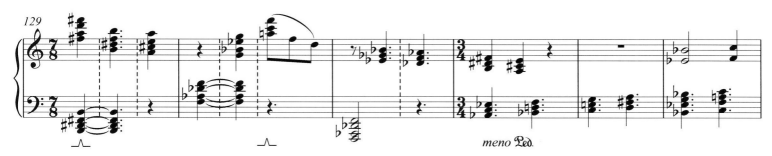

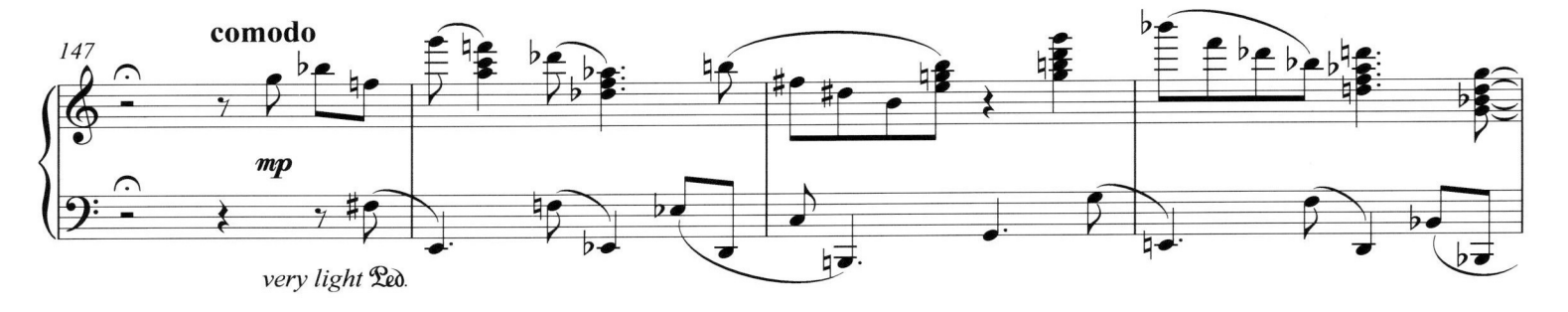

very light Ped.

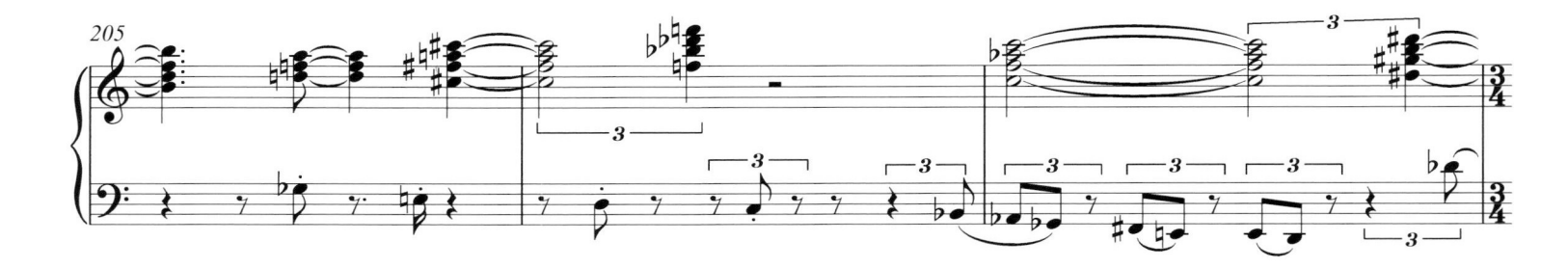

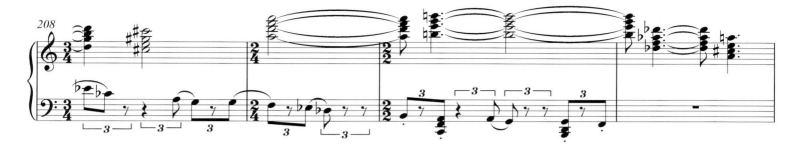

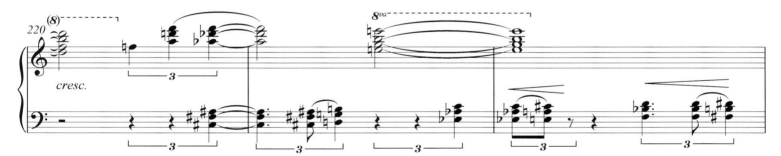

(con Ped.)

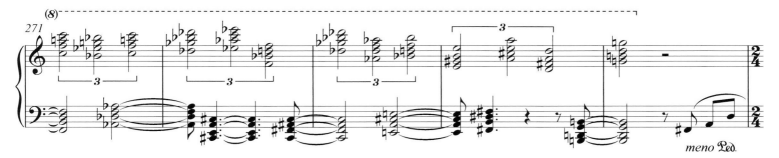

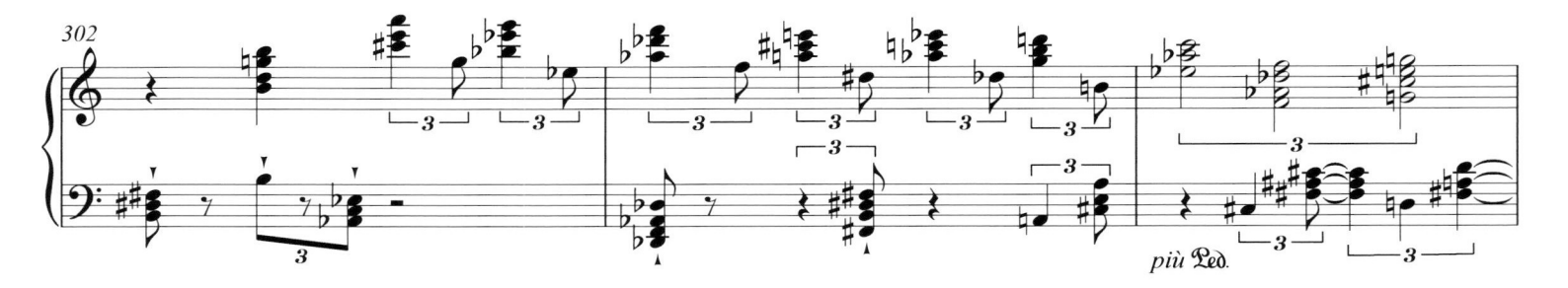